For:

My mother, who never got the chance to share her hopes and dreams with me.

My beautiful, amazing babies who inspire me every day to be a stronger, better person.
Ashlyn, Emma Kate, Reid, and Claire, this book is because of you.

Special thanks to:

My sweet husband and number one fan, John, who always cheers me on.

To every mother out there who has inspired me to be a better mother.
You know who you are.

Homespun Books

Homespun Books, LLC
PO Box 73
Marshall, WA 99020

www.HomeSpunBooks.com

LCCN: 2010906827

ISBN-13: 978-0-9827533-0-9

Book design by Mike Lee

Edited by G. Paul Miller

The illustrations for this book are rendered in oil pastel by Shari Bartels.

As a Mom...

By Shari Bartels

As a Mom,
I hope you have the chance to succeed...

and the opportunity to fail,

because without a little failure
there is no real success.

I hope you respect authority and gain knowledge from that experience...

but question everything, with absolute boldness.

I hope you have the ambition to work hard,
so hard that your hands are calloused
and your muscles ache...

and you find joy in reaping the reward
and share it if you choose.

As a Mom, I hope you value life...

and accept the fact that everything changes.

I hope that each time you hear the Pledge of Allegiance, you put your hand on your heart, and feel the message,

and that you understand the miracle of
how this country was made.

As a Mom, I hope you learn to do the right thing…

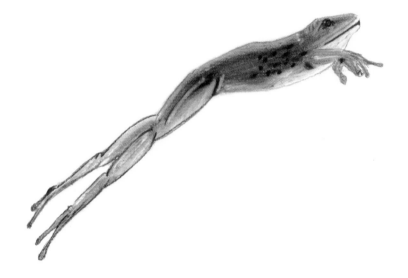

and to understand that the right thing
is not always the easiest thing.

I hope you experience all the adventure and beauty in nature…

but respect its enormous danger.

I hope you learn to take risks,
and throw caution to the wind,

but also realize that sometimes
you might end up with a scar.

I hope you experience a love so deep
and intense that it almost hurts,

but if you endure a loss so profound
that it shakes your soul,

you discover the strength of your spirit.

I hope you learn to appreciate honor,

and to study history, never forgetting its lessons.

As a Mom, I hope when you are wronged
you will learn to forgive,

and will have the grace to move on without bitterness.

I hope you have the ability
to laugh at yourself,

yet are respected for the way you live.

I hope that you speak without fear
and mean the words you say,

and are careful to say
only what you mean.

As a Mom, I hope that you treasure your family more than anything else,

but understand that we may not
always see things the same way.

I hope you know that there is something
bigger than you in this life...

but to me, you are

Everything.

About the Author

Shari Bartels was inspired to write *As a Mom* while listening to news events unfold on the radio as she was parked in her car waiting for her children to be dismissed from school. In a world busy with the hustle, relativisms and uncertainty, she thought it was important to write down the things she most wanted her children to learn and experience that might help them lead noble and honorable lives. On the back of a receipt she found amongst sippy cups and discarded grocery lists she scratched down some hopes for her children, as a Mom. After persistent encouragement from her husband, she decided to share the tale with other Moms in a hope that it would open up conversations with them and their children.

Shari was raised on a dairy farm in Castle Rock, Washington. She graduated from Washington State University, and now lives near Spokane, Washington, with her husband and four children. In her spare time, she enjoys gardening, home projects and spending time with her animals, family, and friends.